Edition Schott

Nikolai Kapustin

Николай Капустин

1937 – 2020

Sleight of Hand

(2009)

for Piano
für Klavier
для фортепиано

opus 138

Authorized Version

ED 23388
ISMN 979-0-001-21229-8

www.schott-music.com

Mainz · London · Madrid · Paris · New York · Tokyo · Beijing

Sleight of Hand
opus 138

Nikolai Kapustin
1937–2020